Contents

Highlights®
Puzzle Buzz®

Can you find this buzzing bee?

It is hiding 5 times on the cover.

COVER ILLUSTRATION BY MARK COLLINS

Concert Maze

START

Help Frieda meet up with her friends. Find a clear path from START to FINISH. Do not go past anything blocking your way.

FINISH

Answer on page 30

Hidden Pictures

Can you find these 12 items hidden at the skate park?

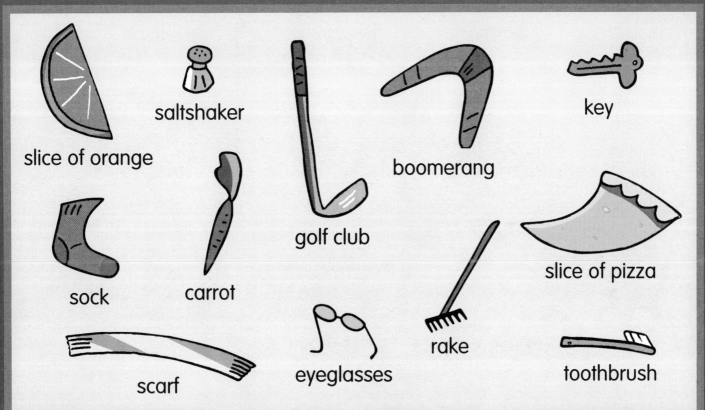

slice of orange

saltshaker

golf club

boomerang

key

sock

carrot

slice of pizza

scarf

eyeglasses

rake

toothbrush

Dot to Dot

Connect the dots from 1 to 45 to see another fun ride.

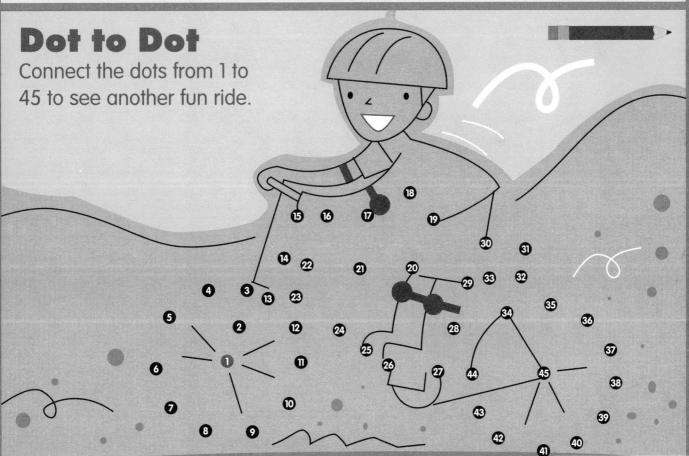

5

Bow Search

This dog show has plenty of bows!
Can you find 20 in the picture?

Can you find?
Two of the dogs look the same. Can you find them?

ILLUSTRATION BY SCOTT BURROUGHS

EST IN HOW

7

Double Tag

Tag—you're it! These pictures are a bit different.
Add stickers to this page to make them match.

9

Answer on page 31

Wiggle Pictures

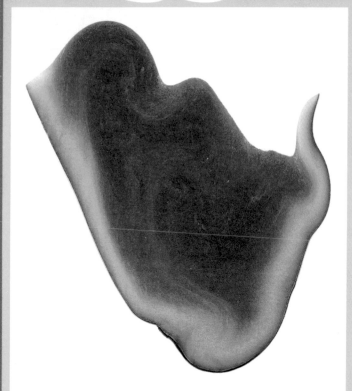

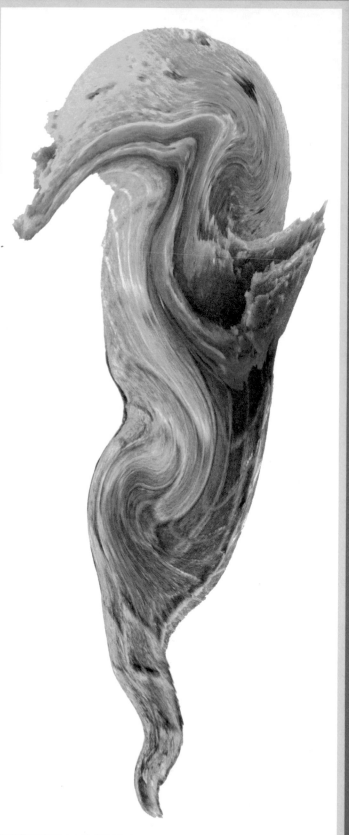

These sweet treats have been twisted and turned. Can you figure out what each one is?

Art Starters

Fill-in Fun
Color each space that has a dot to see a busy buzzer.

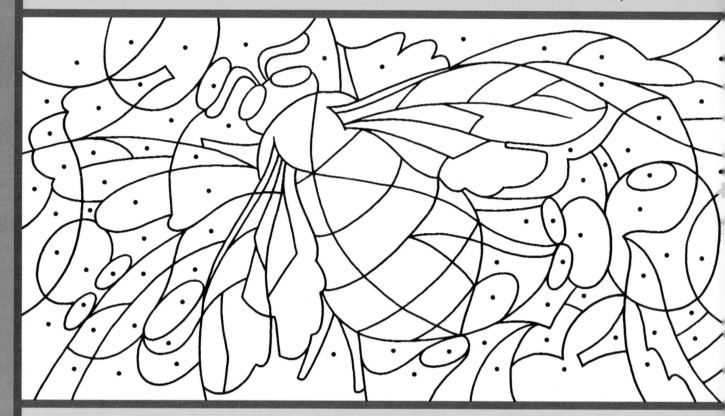

Color Copy
Use markers or crayons to make an alien that matches.

ILLUSTRATION BY RON ZALME

Step by Step Follow the steps to draw a motorcycle.

1.

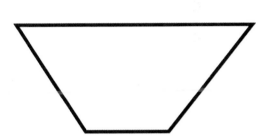

2.

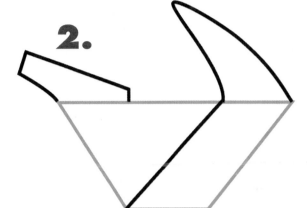

3.

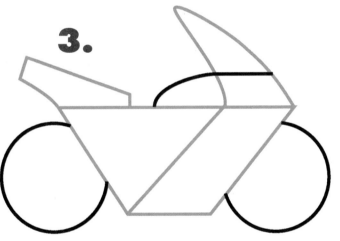

4.

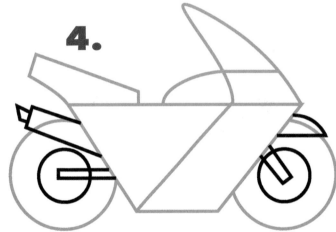

5.

Answer on page 31

Match Maker

Highlights Puzzle BuZz

Every plane in the picture has one that looks just like it. Find all 10 matching pairs.

ILLUSTRATION BY DAVE JOLY

15

Answer on page 31

What's Wrong?®

Use your stickers to finish the picture. Then see if you can find at least 15 silly things.

ILLUSTRATION BY SEAN PARKES

Try 10

1. Name three kinds of flowers.

2. What time of day is the sun highest in the sky?
○ 9 a.m.   ○ noon   ○ 5 p.m.

3. Each star on the United States flag stands for a president.
○ True   ○ False

5. Circle the necklace with more beads.

4. The word "blanco" is Spanish for which color?
○ black   ○ white   ○ blue

6. Name two words that rhyme with pole.

7. The shamrock is a symbol for which holiday?
○ Earth Day
○ Valentine's Day
○ St. Patrick's Day

8. Circle the seventh letter of the alphabet.

g i h

9. Dog paddle, backstroke, and crawl are all types of what activity?

10. Strawberries grow on trees.
○ True   ○ False

Answer on page 31

Ride On!

SPEED COASTER

ROXIE

RUSTY

Highlights Puzzle BuZz

Roxie, Rusty, and Roy are ready to ride! Follow the paths to see where each is headed.

ILLUSTRATION BY DAVID COULSON

Countdown

OBJECTS BY RITA LASCARO

23

Answer on page 32

On the Farm

It's feeding time at the farm. Find all the hidden objects.
Place a sticker on each one.

25

Answer on page 32

Beach Find

The names of 18 beach things are hidden in the letters. Some words are across. Others are up and down. We found SHOVEL. Can you find the rest?

Word List

BALL
BREEZE
CHAIR
FLIP-FLOPS
HAT
OCEAN
PAIL
SAND
SEA GULL
SEAWEED
SHELL
~~SHOVEL~~
STARFISH
SUN
SWIMSUIT
TOWEL
TREE
WAVE

```
K O C E A N B A L L
X J K S H E L L F H
J Q S E A G U L L A
Y X S W I M S U I T
T O W E L S H S P B
R Y A C J U O A F R
E Q V H X N V N L E
E S E A W E E D O E
Y P A I L X L K P Z
S T A R F I S H S E
```

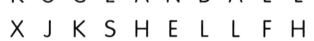

Beach Fun Draw a summer sand castle here.

Answer on page 32

G Is For ?

Can you find a glove, a goat, and a goldfish? What other things can you find that begin with the letter G?

ILLUSTRATION BY DAVE KLUG

Tongue Twister

Try to say this three times as fast as you can: **Gray geese graze in the green grass.**

Answer on page 32

Answers

Cover

2. Concert Maze

Two of a Kind

4. Hidden Pictures®

5. Dot to Dot

6. Bow Search

Answers

8. Double Tag

10. Wiggle Pictures

watermelon

cupcake strawberry

jelly beans ice-cream cone banana split

12. Fill-in Fun

It's a bumblebee!

14. Match Maker

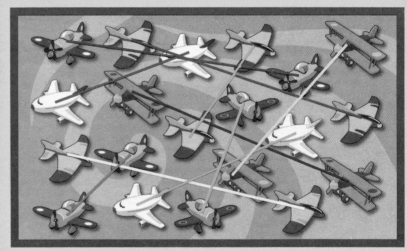

16. What's Wrong?®

Here are the things we found. You may have found others.

18. Try 10

1. Tulips, roses, and daffodils
   Did you think of others?
2. Noon
3. False. Each star stands for a state.
4. White
5. Circle the necklace on the right.
6. Mole and troll
7. St. Patrick's Day
8. Circle the g.
9. Swimming
10. False

Answers

20. Ride On!

22. Countdown

24. On the Farm

26. Beach Find

```
K O C E A N B A L L
X J K S H E L L F H
J Q S E A G U L L A
Y X S W I M S U I T
T O W E L S H S P B
R Y A C J U O A F R
E Q V H X N V N L E
E S E A W E E D O E
Y P A I L X L K P Z
S T A R F I S H S E
```

28. G Is For ?

Here are the G words we found.
You may have found others.

1. gift
2. gate
3. giant
4. game
5. gown
6. glass
7. ghost
8. grass
9. globe
10. goose

11. guitar
12. geyser
13. garage
14. gorilla
15. grapes
16. glasses
17. giraffe
18. garden
19. goggles
20. golf club

21. golf ball
22. Goldilocks
23. grapefruit
24. groundhog
25. gas pump
26. green beans
27. grasshopper
28. garbage can
29. garbage truck

What Is It?

It's the Statue of Liberty
and fireworks!

32